# *Changing Partners*

## *Exercises*

## *Photocopy Master*

**Brown and Brown**

Publishers:   Brown and Brown,
              Keeper's Cottage,
              Westward,
              Wigton,
              Cumbria  CA7 8NQ
              Tel. 016973 42915

First published 1997

ISBN 1 870596 65 X

Printed by Reed's Ltd., Penrith, Cumbria on Corona 100%
recycled paper and SylvanPrint 100% recycled card.

# Introduction

This set of exercises is to be used in conjunction with the book *Changing Partners*. Although the exercises may be photocopied, subject to the restrictions below, the book may not.

There are 4 pages of exercises for each of the 5 chapters and 10 pages of general exercises on the book as a whole. The text of *Changing Partners* is fairly simple and most of the exercises are designed to improve reading, spelling and vocabulary skills. *Sections G & H* of the *General Exercises* aim to stimulate writing and discussion, although there are other, more limited, opportunities for this in earlier sections. Students should not necessarily be expected to answer every question in every exercise.

Most of the answers to the exercises can be found in the text but answers to *General Exercises, Sections A, B & C* are given on *p.36*.

*For a catalogue of publications, please contact:*
Brown and Brown, Keeper's Cottage, Westward, Wigton,
Cumbria CA7 8NQ                    *Tel. 016973 42915*

# Contents

# Chapter 1 : Julie    *Exercises*

**A.**   **Fill in the missing words**

*Fill in your own word and then compare it with the one used in the book.*

1.  I didn't think it would _____ to us.

2.  When we were first married it was _____ .

3.  After a year or _____ , we moved to a small house.

4.  Kevin, my husband, _____ as a salesman.

5.  After a while, we decided to _____ a family.

6.  _____ a few months it didn't seem so bad.

7.  I went back to work for a _____ of afternoons each week.

8.  Things _____ seemed to get worse and worse.

9.  It was as if we had _____ being friends.

10. Eventually Kevin got his licence _____ and a new job.

## B. Tick the right answer

*Try to answer the questions without looking back at the book.*

1. How long was Julie married ?

   **a.** 8 years  **b.** 10 years  **c.** 12 years

2. Where did Julie work ?

   **a.** Bank  **b.** Shop  **c.** Building Society

3. What is the name of her daughter ?

   **a.** Rebecca  **b.** Rachel  **c.** Betty

4. What is the name of her son ?

   **a.** Lee  **b.** Lewis  **c.** Liam

5. What was the name of the firm that took over Kevin's old firm, Office Systems ?

   **a.** P.L.C. Ltd.  **b.** E.P.L. Ltd.

   **c.** E.E.C. Ltd.

6. Where was Kevin based with the new firm ?

   **a.** Liverpool  **b.** London  **c.** Leeds

7. What did Kevin sell in his new job after he got his driving licence back ?

   **a.** Double glazing  **b.** Conservatories

   **c.** Insurance

## C. Words and Phrases

1. *a.* *Give another word or phrase which means much the same as the highlighted word in each of these sentences:*

   I was **expecting** Rebecca.

   He still had to **cover** the same area.

   He was **based** in Leeds.

   Kevin was **stuck** in Leeds.

   I talked a lot to her about **coping** as a single parent.

   It's been **hard** for the kids.

   *b.* *Use each word in a sentence of your own. If possible, give the word a slightly different meaning from the example given above.*

2. *Can you think of another phrase or word which means much the same as each of these ?*

   **cut-throat** (business)

   **bringing up** (a family)

   **a bit of a bombshell**

   **drifting along**

   **sweep things under the carpet**

# D. Spelling

1. *Looking quickly through Julie's story:*

   a. *Find at least 5 words which contain the sound and spelling '**er**'.*

   b. *Find at least 5 words which contain the sound '**aw**' (e.g. as in **law**; **bore**; **pour**). How many different spellings of the sound '**aw**' can you find?*

2. a. *Make lists of the words in Julie's story which contain **c** (as in **ice**) and **c** (as in **coat**).*

   b. *Look at the 2 lists carefully, and say the words aloud. Can you make a spelling rule about when **c** sounds like **s** and when it sounds like **k** in a word?*

3. *Sort out these jumbled words from Julie's story:*

   yad     layler     flyaim     lyon     undysled

   moyen     yulck     swayal     coyiest     yawa

   *What do all the words have in common?*

4. *Write down as many words of 2 or more letters as you can make from the letters in:*

   **BREATHALYSED**

# Chapter 2 : Kevin    *Exercises*

## A.    Fill in the missing words

*Fill in your own word and then compare it with the one used in the book.*

1.  I was under a lot of _____ at work.

2.  There's something wrong with the _____ .

3.  I _____ what it's like being out of work.

4.  I wasn't a _____ like some of them.

5.  I tried to keep _____ doing up the house.

6.  _____ has to be just as she wants it.

7.  I was working _____ evenings and weekends.

8.  I don't know anyone else who still gets on with their _____ .

9.  I've got a steady _____ now.

10. _____ it gets to me because of things they say.

## B. Answer these questions

1. Was Kevin expecting that he and Julie would separate ?

2. What did he think was the cause of the break-up of their marriage ?

3. What was Kevin doing on the day that he got breathalysed ?

4. Why did the police breathalyse him ?

5. What was his reaction when Julie told him that she wanted them to split up ?

6. What problems did he have after the break-up ?

7. How often does he see the children ?

8. In what ways does he feel that the relation-ship between him and Julie isn't too bad ?

9. What does Kevin say about Chrissy and her daughter, Nicola ?

10. What does he think about Julie's partner, Steve ?

# C. Words and Phrases

1. **a.** *Give another word or phrase which means much the same as the highlighted word in each of these sentences:*

   They're always on at you to **make** this or that target.

   This one was in a **fancy** hotel.

   I wasn't a **boozer**.

   It was a **foul** night.

   I've got a **steady** girlfriend now.

   Her ex-husband is a **nutter**.

   **b.** *Use each word in a sentence of your own. If possible, give the word a slightly different meaning from the example given above.*

2. *Can you think of another phrase or word which means much the same as each of these?*

   **under a lot of pressure**

   **old boy**

   **kicked out** (job)

   **doing up** (house)

   **finding fault**

   **being apart from**

## D. Spelling

1. *Looking quickly through Kevin's story:*

   **a.** *Find at least 5 words which end in **-ing**.*

   **b.** *Find at least 5 words which contain double vowels making one sound (e.g. **ee**).*

2. **a.** *Find words in Kevin's story which sound the same as each of the words below but have a different spelling and meaning.*

   | | | | | |
   |---|---|---|---|---|
   | their | new | ours | brakes | farther |
   | knot | no | weigh | two | councillor |

   **b.** *Put each of the above words into a sentence which explains its meaning.*

3. **a.** *What is the difference between these ?*

   **licence** & **license**

   **councillor** & **counsellor**

4. *Write out each of these in full:*

   | | | | | |
   |---|---|---|---|---|
   | I'm | didn't | you've | they're | we'd |
   | can't | I'd | wasn't | I've | there's |

5. *Write down words which can be made from the word below without changing the order of the letters:*

   **DEVASTATED**

# Chapter 3 : Stephen *Exercises*

## A. Fill in the missing words

*Fill in your own word and then compare it with the one used in the book.*

1. I first met Julie at the Theatre Club some _____ ago.

2. She met this _____ professor over there.

3. I had lived _____ for a long time.

4. I _____ this house about ten years ago.

5. The _____ is falling apart, but it feels comfortable.

6. They often go to their _____ at weekends.

7. Kevin and I get on fairly well, _____ .

8. I don't want him _____ that I favour Becky.

9. Becky's supposed to be at the _____ age.

10. She and Julie can usually find something to _____ about.

# B. Answer these questions

1. How did Stephen and Julie get to know each other ?

2. Do you think it was a case of "love at first sight" ?

3. In your own words, explain about Stephen and the girl he was engaged to.

4. What names would you suggest for her and her American husband ?

5. What picture do you have in your mind of Stephen's house ?

6. When Julie and the kids moved in with Stephen, what effect did it have on his life ?

7. How does Stephen get on with Kevin ?

8. How does Stephen get on with Liam ?

9. How does Stephen get on with Becky ?

10. What impression do you get of the relationship between Julie and Becky ?

## C. Words and Phrases

1. *Give another word or phrase which means much the same as the highlighted word in each of these sentences:*

   Julie's a **wonderful** person.

   It's been **strange** suddenly becoming part of a family.

   The place is falling apart, but it feels **comfortable**.

   Becky's supposed to be at the **awkward** age.

   She can be a bit **temperamental**.

   They have a really **outstanding** Director.

2. *Can you think of another phrase or word which means much the same as each of these ?*

   **moved in**

   **falling apart**

   **a bit of a break**

   **a lot in common**

   **take an interest in**

# D.  Spelling

1.  *Looking quickly through Stephen's story:*

    **a.**  *Find at least 5 words which begin with 2
    consonants making one sound.  (e.g. **sh**)*

    **b.**  *Find at least 5 words which begin with 2
    consonants making separate sounds.
    (e.g. **pl**)*

2.  *Think of a word which sounds the same as each
    of these words from Stephen's story but has a
    different spelling and meaning:*

    some      would      meet      been      place

    through      hear      find      right      in

3.  *Fill in the correct word in each sentence:*

    **a.**  They're _____ a talented group.
    *(quiet / quite)*

    **b.**  They often go to _____ Dad at weekends.
    *(their / there)*

    **c.**  _____ different now that _____ all
    one big family home.
    *(its / it's)*

    **d.**  I was giving the chorus extra _____ .
    *(practise / practice)*

    **e.**  Most of the time they are all _____ .
    *(write / right / rite)*

# Chapter 4 : Becky    *Exercises*

## A.    Fill in the missing words

*Fill in your own word and then compare it with the one used in the book.*

1.  I want to be an _____ .

2.  They give her the leads because she's blonde and has _____ legs.

3.  She really fancies herself (and most of the _____ ).

4.  In _____ life she's only a trainee hairdresser.

5.  Steve's my mum's _____ .

6.  He _____ all about plays and music.

7.  We're doing *West Side Story* next _____ .

8.  He talks to me _____ an adult.

9.  He's always reading and he uses these _____ words.

10. Without her _____ would get done.

# B. Answer these questions

*Try to answer the questions without looking back at the book.*

1. How old is Becky ?

   **a.** 12     **b.** 13     **c.** 14

2. What is the name of Becky's drama group ?

3. Why does Becky think that Olivia Mellor gets the best parts ?

4. What nickname do they give Olivia ?

5. What shows does the Queen's Hall Theatre Club put on in a year ?

6. What sort of parts does Becky's mum usually get ?

7. What sort of actress does Becky want to be ?

8. What trip did Becky go on with her mum and Steve ?

9. How does Becky get on with Steve, do you think ?

10. What does Becky say about her mum's character ?

## C.    Words and Phrases

1.    *Give another word or phrase which means much
the same as the highlighted word in each of these
sentences.*

She really *fancies* herself.

In *real* life she's only a trainee hairdresser.

She usually only has the *smaller* parts.

I want to be a *proper* actress.

She was *brilliant*.

He's *great*.

He helps me with my Youth Theatre *stuff*.

She's quite *bossy*.


2.    *Can you think of another phrase or word which
means much the same as each of these ?*

**O.K.**

**not bad**

**as well**

**most of the time**

**just as well**

## D. Spelling and Grammar

1. *Looking quickly through Becky's story:*

   **a.** *Find at least 5 words which contain double consonants making one sound (e.g. **dd**).*

   **b.** *Find at least 5 words which contain a pair of vowels making one sound (e.g. **ea**, **ou**).*

2. **a.** *All these words from Becky's story end in '**s**'. Which are nouns and which are verbs ?*

   gets     helps     boys     musicals

   knows     words     fancies     does

   **b.** *Make up sentences using each of these words as a noun and then as a verb:*

   plays     talks     calls     treats     uses

3. *Put apostrophes into these sentences where they are needed:*

   **a.** Im nearly 14.

   **b.** Shes blonde and has long legs.

   **c.** Ive had one or two kids parts with them.

   **d.** Steves my Mums boyfriend.

   **e.** Hes always reading and he uses these long words.

   **f.** They do 3 or 4 plays and musicals every year.

# Chapter 5 : Liam    *Exercises*

## A.    Fill in the missing words

*Fill in your own word and then compare it with the one used in the book.*

1. I've only _____ there a few weeks.

2. She's two years _____ of me.

3. He' a _____ goalkeeper.

4. She says we have to call him her _____ .

5. _____ got this big room all to myself.

6. Steve's _____ at practical things.

7. And he comes to _____ me play when he can.

8. We _____ go and see them on Sundays.

9. She's always got the latest CD or _____ .

10. I wish Mum and Dad were _____ together.

# B.    Answer these questions

1.  Which school does Liam go to ?

2.  Which year is Liam in and which year is his older sister in ?

3.  What do you think is Liam's main interest ?

4.  Write down last week's soccer result as it would have appeared on the Sports noticeboard ?

5.  What does Liam say about the term *partner* ?

6.  What does Liam think of Steve's house ?

7.  What does Liam think of Steve ?

8.  How does Liam get on with his dad ?

9.  Describe what Liam would usually do at the weekend ?

10.  Why does Liam hate Nicola ?

## C. Words and Phrases

1. *Think of another word or phrase which means much the same as the highlighted word in each of these sentences.*

   The school soccer's **really** good.

   My mum moved in with her **bloke**, Steve.

   But I think it sounds **daft**.

   It's **freezing** in winter.

   He **runs** the library.

   He **shouts** at her when she has it on loud.

   Dad's always mending or making things, or **fixing** the car.

   The **trouble** is, she doesn't like football.

   I **hate** her.

2. *Can you think of another phrase or word which means much the same as each of these ?*

   **ahead of**

   **got into** (team)

   **a couple of**

   **stay over**

   **put up with**

## D. Spelling

1. *Looking quickly through Liam's story:*

   **a.** *Find 5 words which contain the sound and spelling **ar**.*

   **b.** *Find 5 words which contain the spelling **ou**. What sound does **ou** make in each word ?*

2. *Fill in the missing letters.*

   **a.** I've just started at Rushw____th Comp.

   **b.** He played some Lea____e matches for Y____k City.

   **c.** It sounds as if they're in bu____ness.

   **d.** We leave h____ behind on Sat____day aft____noons.

   **e.** He runs the lib____ry at the University.

   **f.** I us____lly stay over at his flat.

   **g.** She's got this stupid dau____ter called Nicola.

   **h.** He c____es to w____ch me play when he can.

3. *How many words can you think of which begin with the same prefix as these ?*

   **a.** Reserves *(re-)*

   **b.** behind *(be-)*

# General Exercises

*(Exercises on all 5 Chapters)*

**A.** **Can you remember who did what ?**

1.  Who worked in a Building Society ?

2.  Who worked for *Office Systems* ?

3.  Who was born on St. Valentine's Day ?

4.  Who was breathalysed with Kevin ?

5.  Who said it was important for children to carry on seeing their father ?

6.  Who is a 'nutter' ?

7.  Who got a job in Germany ?

8.  Who now lives in Seattle ?

9.  Who is a University librarian ?

10. Who used to live in a flat in Stephen's house ?

11. Who likes cars, soccer and making things ?

12. Who is said to be at 'the awkward age' ?

13. Who is an 'outstanding Director' ?

14. Who is a trainee hairdresser ?

15. Who was brilliant in a West End play ?

16. Who talks to Becky like an adult ?

17. Who is said to treat Becky as if she was 8 ?

18. Who played for the City Reserves and for York City ?

19. Who takes Liam to watch City play ?

20. Who has got a daughter called Nicola ?


## B.   Long and short names

1. Write out a list of all the first names used in the book.

2. Put the list into alphabetical order.

3. Which of the names are shortened and what is the full version of each name ?

4. Which of the names do you think could not be shortened ?

# C. Find the word

*Using the clues below, fill in the 8 words in the grid to find the word in the shaded boxes.*

1. What Kevin and Julie were for 12 years
2. A person one knows and likes (of either sex)
3. Some people fall in _____ at first sight
4. Two people; a pair
5. A person you live with in a relationship
6. A son or daughter
7. Not married
8. Marriage ceremony

*Changing Partners: Exercises General*

## D. it's *or* its ?

*Add apostrophes to the highlighted words where they are needed.*

1. You don't know what *its* like in sales until you've done it.

2. *Its* been hard for the kids at times.

3. The Youth Theatre is great - especially *its* Director.

4. I know what *its* like being out of work.

5. I go to Rushworth Comp. *Its* soccer team is really good.

6. *Its* changed my life completely.

7. *Its* different now that *its* all one big family home.

8. *Its* got 3 floors and an attic.

9. *Its* a pity it hasn't got *its* own swimming pool as well.

10. Divorce has *its* problems but *its* worked out O.K. for us.

# E. How many words can you list ?

1. *Make a list of all the words or phrases that you can think of which can be used for these:*

   **a.** Two people who are going out together

   **b.** Getting married

   **c.** What a wife might call her husband

   **d.** How a husband might refer to his wife

   **e.** When a married couple stop living together

   **f.** When an unmarried couple live with each other

   **g.** The name of the other person when you live with them

   **h.** Making love

2. *If Stephen was a politician or other well-known person, what names would the newspapers use to describe:*

   **a.** Stephen ?

   **b** Julie ?

   **c.** The house they live in ?

## F.   Add an ending

*How many different words can you make by adding endings to the words below ?*

> **Example**
>
> **back**   *backs; backed; backing; backer; background; backache; backfire; backside; backslider; backwards*

1. **Work**

2. **Act**

3. **Flat**

4. **Play**

5. **Expect**

6. **Marry** *(the final y can be changed to i)*

7. **House** *(the final e can be dropped)*

8. **Relate** *(the final e can be dropped)*

# G. Writing and Discussion

## About the book

*The suggestions and questions in this section are designed to encourage students to read between the lines and to make their own judgements about the characters and their situation.*

1. What do you think were the reasons for Julie and Kevin's divorce ?

2. Write a few sentences showing how each of the 5 writers has been affected by the divorce ?

3. Would it have been better for the family if Julie and Kevin had stayed together ?

4. Why do you think Nicola, Chrissy's daughter, is always boasting about her new clothes or her latest CD or video ?

5. Choose a person in the story who interests you and write a description of them and their personality.

6. **a.** Which of the people in the book do you think you would get on best with ? Say why.

   **b.** Which of the people in the book do you think you would not get on with ? Say why.

7. Write a phone conversation between Kevin and Julie about arrangements for the children to stay at Kevin's over the weekend.

8. Write a conversation between each of the couples below as if they had just come across each other in the High Street:

   **a.** Stephen and Kevin

   **b.** Julie and Chrissy

   **c.** Liam and Nicola

9. Write a sixth chapter for the book from the point of view of Chrissy or Nicola.

10. Do you think it is likely that Julie and Stephen and Kevin and Chrissy will stay together for the rest of their lives ? Say why.

# H.  Writing and Discussion

## General

*The suggestions and questions in this section are intended to stimulate writing and discussion on the wider issues related to marriage, divorce and the family.*

1.  It is often said that in the old days married couples generally stayed together and that today they separate or re-marry too quickly.

    Do you think it is a good thing that couples don't stay together if either of the partners is unhappy - or do you think it would be better if they tried harder to make the marriage work ?

2.  Why should anyone get married at all ? Would it not be better if everyone just lived together ?

3.  If couples do not have children, should divorce be easier for them than in marriages where there are children ?

4.  Do you think it is better for children to be brought up by two parents rather than just one ?

**5.** Should it be possible for couples of the same sex to get 'married', to bring up children and to have the same legal rights as other married couples ?

**6.** Do you think it is a good idea to have a Child Support Agency ? Should both parents always be made to support their children financially ?

**7.** Do you think it is a good idea to have a Marriage Guidance Service ? Should it be compulsory for all couples to talk to a Counsellor before getting a divorce ?

**8.** The Courts usually decide that a mother should get custody of her children. Is this right ?

**9.** Describe a family you know that has split up. How have the parents and the children come out of it ?

**10.** Describe a successful marriage that you know. What has made it work ?

# Answers

## General Exercises

### A. Can you remember who did what ?
1. Julie    2. Kevin    3. Liam
4. An old boy in a Jag.
5. Marriage Guidance Counsellor
6. Chrissy's ex-husband
7. Stephen's former fiancée
8. Stephen's former fiancée & her American husband
9. Stephen    10. Students    11. Kevin
12. Becky    13. Director of Rushworth Youth Theatre
14. Olivia Mellor    15. Juliet Stevenson
16. Stephen    17. Julie
18. The P.E. Teacher at Rushworth Comp.
19. Kevin    20. Chrissy

### B. Long and short names
1. Julie; Kevin; Rebecca; Becky; Liam; Valentine; Stephen; Steve; Chrissy; Nicola; Juliet; Olivia
2. Becky; Chrissy; Julie; Juliet; Kevin; Liam; Nicola; Olivia; Rebecca; Stephen; Steve; Valentine
3. Becky:  Rebecca
   Chrissy:  Christine (*or* Christina; Christabel; Christa)
   Steve:  Stephen (*or* Steven)
4. Liam is, perhaps, the only name not often shortened.

### C. Find the word
1. Married    2. Friend    3. Love    4. Couple
5. Partner    6. Child    7. Single    8. Wedding
*Word in shaded boxes:* Divorced

*Changing Partners: Exercises*